Grandpa Wombat's Snore

Little Wombat can hear his Grandpa snoring. He wishes Grandpa would wake up.

Snoore! Snoooore!

"Grandpa, Grandpa, wake up!"
Little Wombat shouts.

Little Wombat bangs the
log like a drum.

Boom! Boom! Boom!

He wanders over to Grandpa.

Little Wombat pokes Grandpa.

Grandpa opens his eyes, then…

Snoore! Snoooore!
Snoooooore!

He tickles Grandpa's nose with a piece of grass.

The snoring stops, then...

Grandpa goes back to sleep!

Snoore! Snoooore!
Snoooooore!

"I'll ask my friends to help me wake him," thinks Little Wombat.

"Green Frog, will you help me wake up Grandpa?" he asks.

"Yes!" says Green Frog.

Croak

Croak

Croak

Little Wombat rushes off
to find his noisiest friends.

"Cockatoo and Kookaburra, will you
help me wake up Grandpa?"

Oo-oo-ah-ah-ha
Squawk

"Yes," they say.

Oo-oo-ah-ah-ha

Squawk

Croak

What a noise!

Grandpa wakes up and scratches himself.

Huh? Huh? Huh?

"Sorry, Grandpa!" says Little Wombat,
"But you snore so loudly that I
couldn't sleep!"

About Wombats

Australia has three types of wombat – the Common Wombat, the Northern Hairy-nosed Wombat and the Southern Hairy-nosed Wombat. The wombats in this story book are Common Wombats. Wombats are about the size of a large, stocky dog. They live in burrows and come out to eat mostly at night. Their diet is mainly grass, shrubs and roots. Baby wombats are nurtured in a pouch that faces backwards, so that when the mother digs a burrow her pouch does not fill up with dirt.